Step it up!

Fun pieces for clarinet grades 1–3

LOUISE CHAMBERLAIN

PIANO ACCOMPANIMENT

First published in 2003 jointly by Faber Music Ltd and Alfred Publishing Co., Inc.
3 Queen Square London WC1N 3AU
Cover design by Shireen Nathoo Design
Music processed by MusicSet 2000
Printed in England by Caligraving Ltd

ISBN 0-571-52178-9

Distributed in the Americas and Australasia by Alfred Publishing Co., Inc.
Distributed throughout the rest of the world by Faber Music Ltd

CD recorded at House of Music Studio
Produced by Louise Chamberlain and Sam Wedgwood
Engineered by Sam Wedgwood

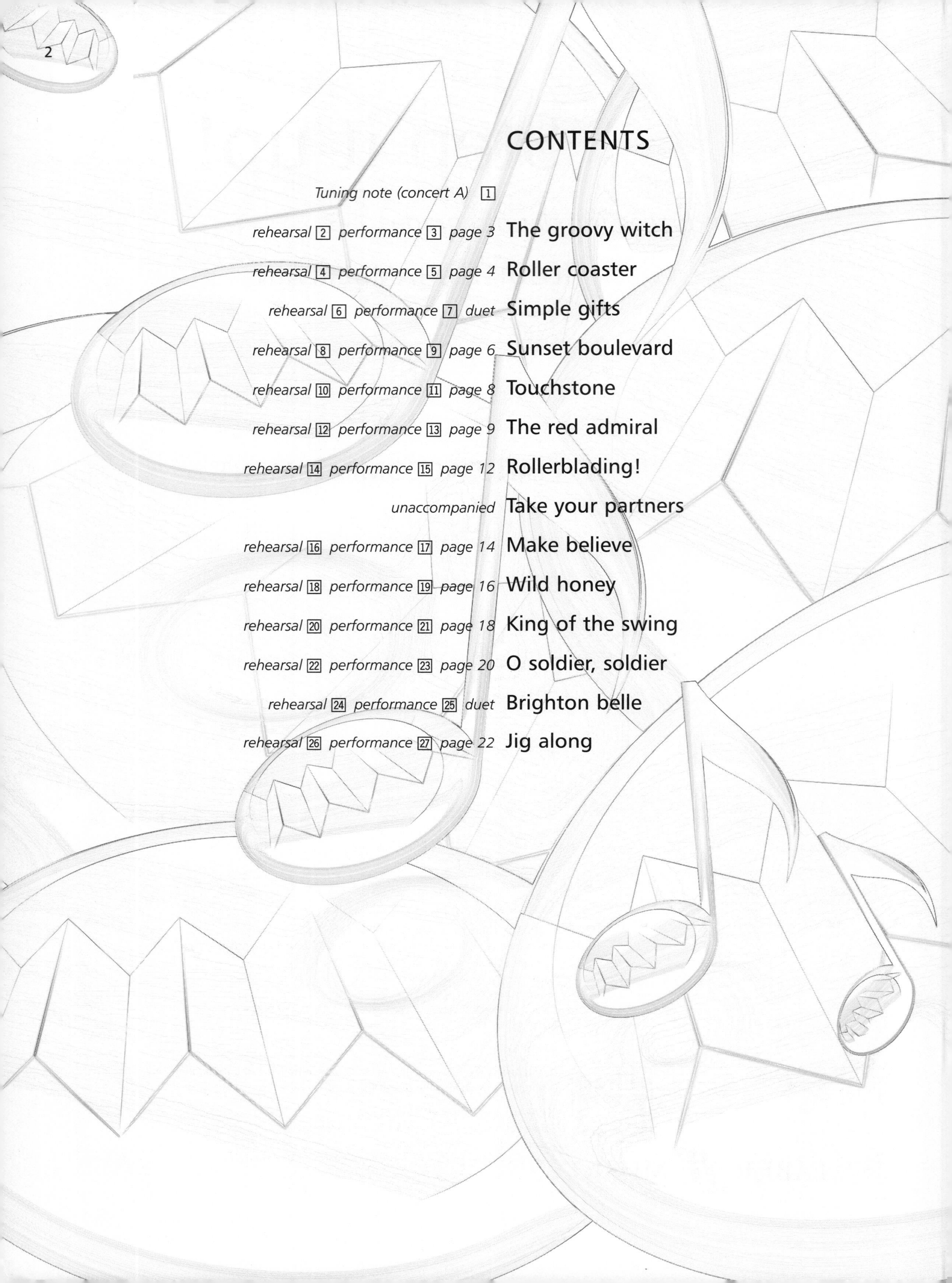

CONTENTS

Tuning note (concert A) [1]

rehearsal [2] *performance* [3] *page 3* The groovy witch

rehearsal [4] *performance* [5] *page 4* Roller coaster

rehearsal [6] *performance* [7] *duet* Simple gifts

rehearsal [8] *performance* [9] *page 6* Sunset boulevard

rehearsal [10] *performance* [11] *page 8* Touchstone

rehearsal [12] *performance* [13] *page 9* The red admiral

rehearsal [14] *performance* [15] *page 12* Rollerblading!

unaccompanied Take your partners

rehearsal [16] *performance* [17] *page 14* Make believe

rehearsal [18] *performance* [19] *page 16* Wild honey

rehearsal [20] *performance* [21] *page 18* King of the swing

rehearsal [22] *performance* [23] *page 20* O soldier, soldier

rehearsal [24] *performance* [25] *duet* Brighton belle

rehearsal [26] *performance* [27] *page 22* Jig along

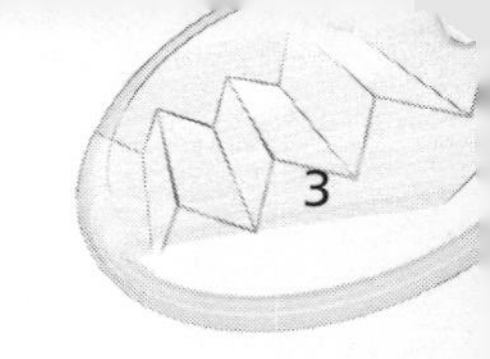

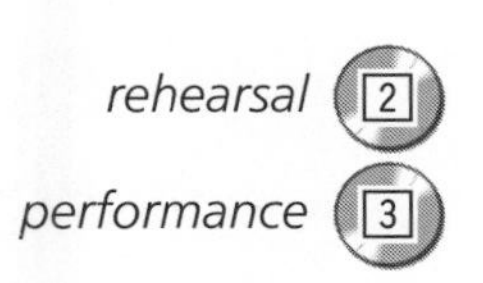

The groovy witch

Louise Chamberlain

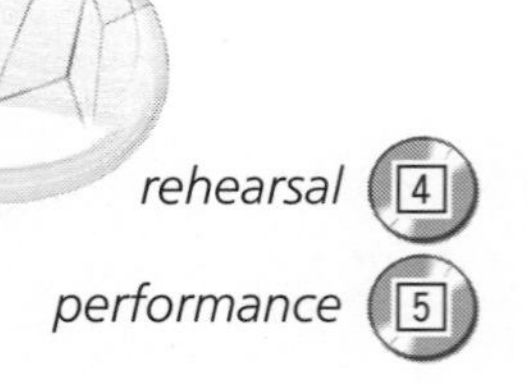

Roller coaster

17
2
mf
mf
20
mf
mf
23
26
f
f

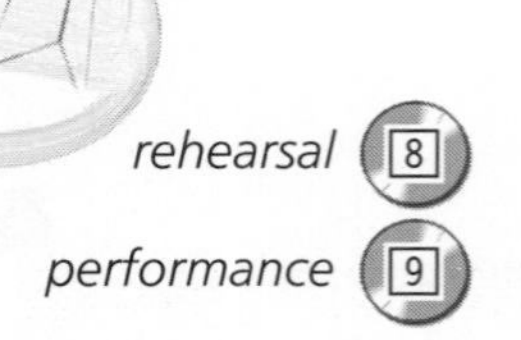

Sunset boulevard

poco rit.
a tempo
p
mf
mp
p
pp

rehearsal 10

performance 11

Touchstone

15
19
D.C. al ⊕
poi al Coda
CODA
poco rit.
rehearsal 12
performance 13
The red admiral
Playfully ♩ = 126
4

8
f
mf
12
mp
mp
16
f
f
20
mp

24
mp
f
28
mp
f
mp
f marcato
32
poco rit.
37
a tempo
mp
p
mp
p

rehearsal 14
performance 15

Rollerblading!

15
mf
f
mf
f
19
mf
mf
23
f
f
26
f
f
p

Make believe

20
f
mp
f
mp
25
f
mp
f
mp
cresc.
30
f
f
f
f
35
p
pp
D.S. 𝄋 al 𝄌
poi al Coda
CODA
cresc.
sfz
cresc.
sfz

rehearsal 18

performance 19

Wild honey

17
mp
mp
21
f
f
mp
mp
25
p
mf
p
mf
29
mp
p
mp
p

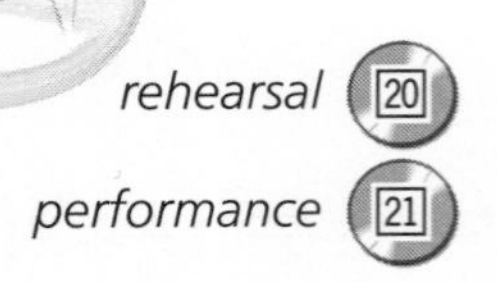

King of the swing

15
p
18
f
f
3
p
22
f
mf
26
p
p
f
f

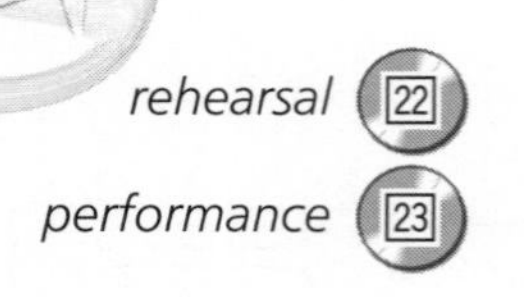

rehearsal 22

performance 23

O soldier, soldier

arr. L.C.

18
mp
p
8va
23
poco rit.
a tempo
f
f
27
30
slower

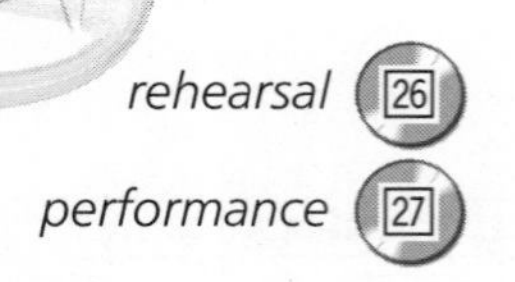
rehearsal 26
performance 27

Jig along

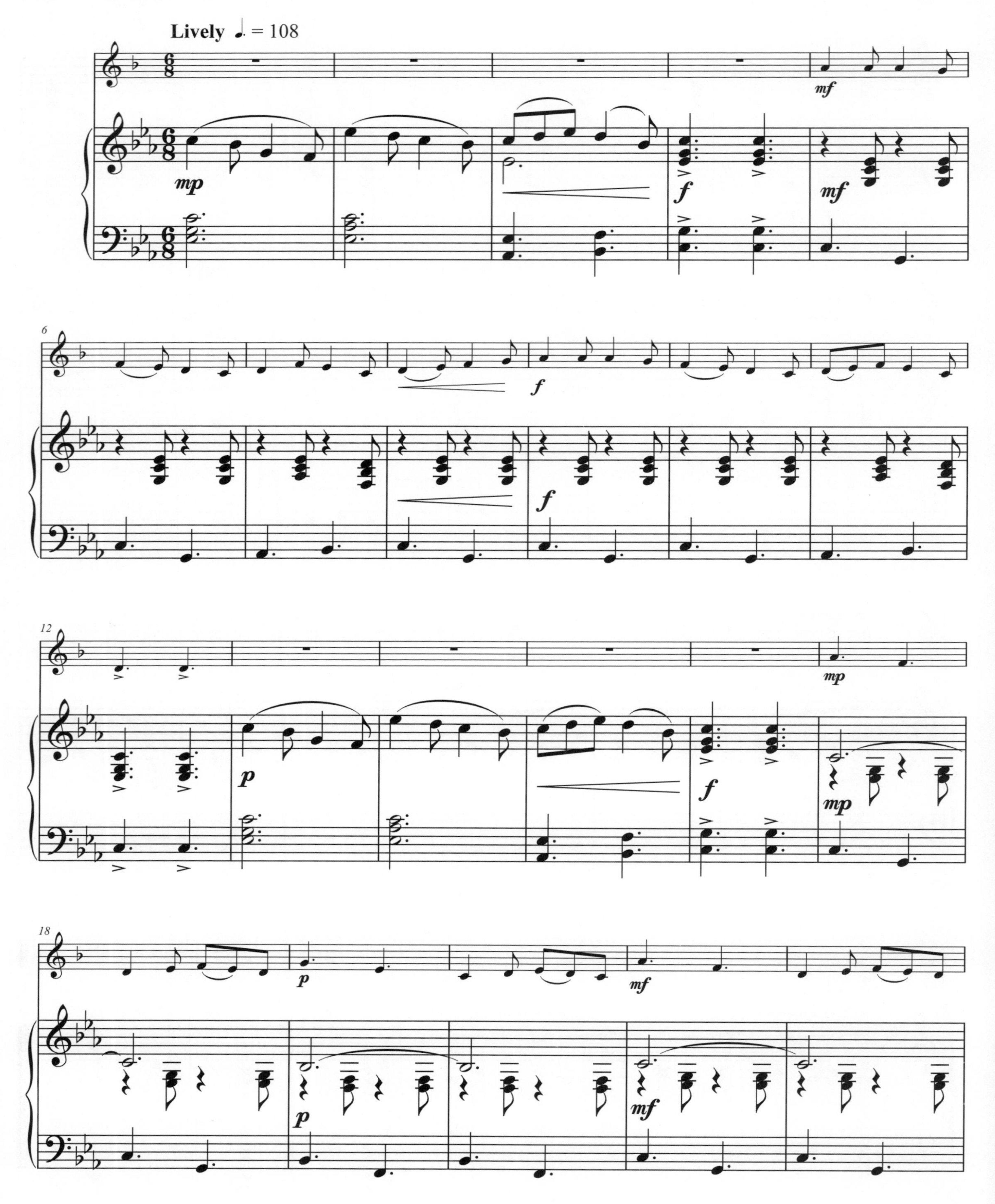
Lively ♩. = 108

23
mf
29
f
f
35
mp
mp
f
f
41
p
p
cresc.
cresc.
f
f

Step it up!

Fun pieces for clarinet grades 1–3

LOUISE CHAMBERLAIN

CLARINET PART

First published in 2003 jointly by Faber Music Ltd and Alfred Publishing Co., Inc.
3 Queen Square London WC1N 3AU
Cover design by Shireen Nathoo Design
Music processed by MusicSet 2000
Printed in England by Caligraving Ltd

ISBN 0-571-52178-9

Distributed in the Americas and Australasia by Alfred Publishing Co., Inc.
Distributed throughout the rest of the world by Faber Music Ltd

CD recorded at House of Music Studio
Produced by Louise Chamberlain and Sam Wedgwood
Engineered by Sam Wedgwood

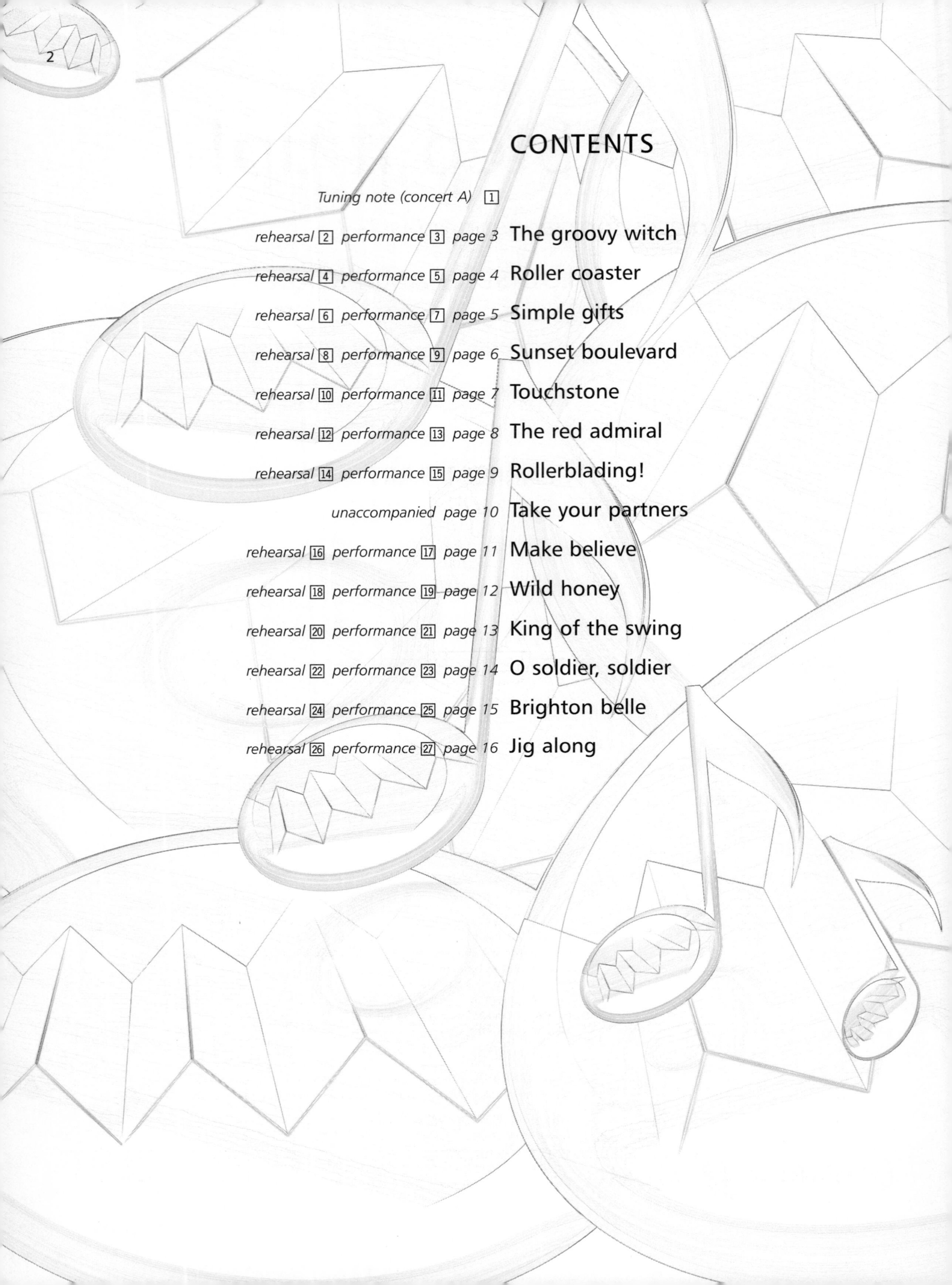

CONTENTS

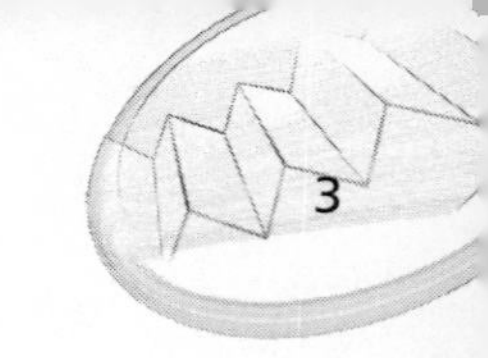

Step it up!

Fun pieces for clarinet grades 1–3

LOUISE CHAMBERLAIN

rehearsal 2
performance 3

The groovy witch

Louise Chamberlain

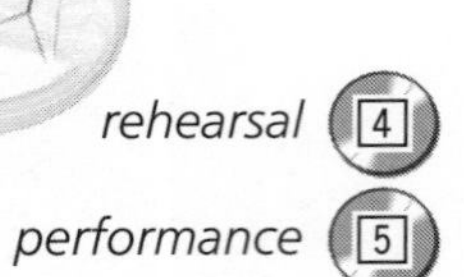

Roller coaster

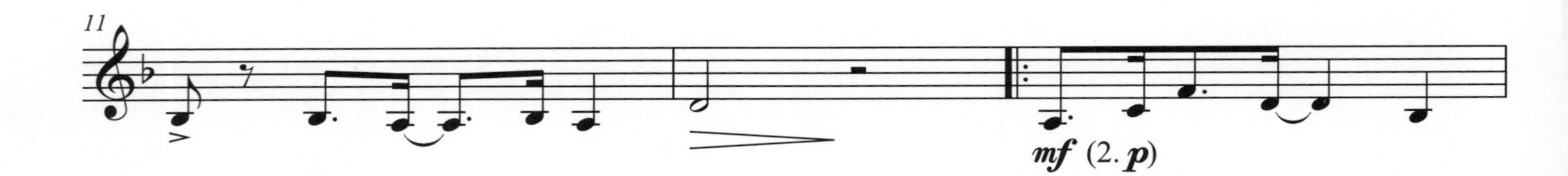

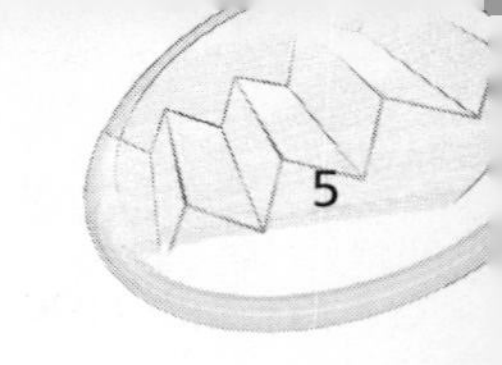

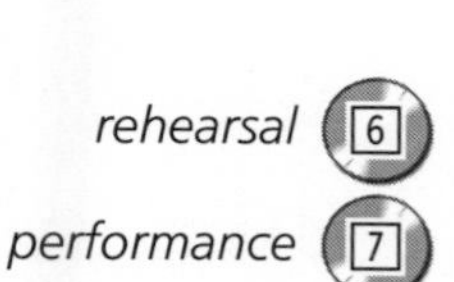

Simple gifts

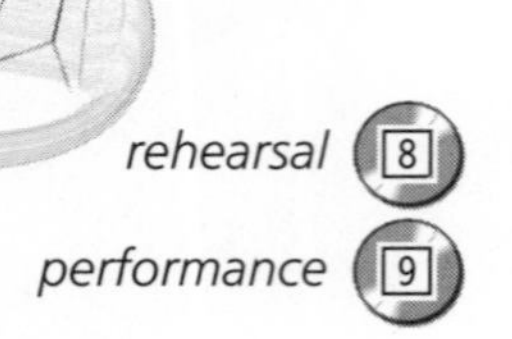

Sunset boulevard

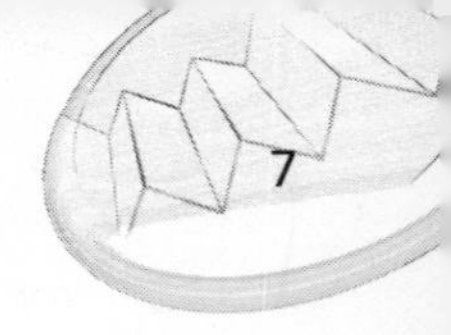

rehearsal 10
performance 11

Touchstone

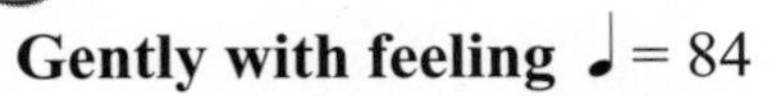
Gently with feeling ♩ = 84

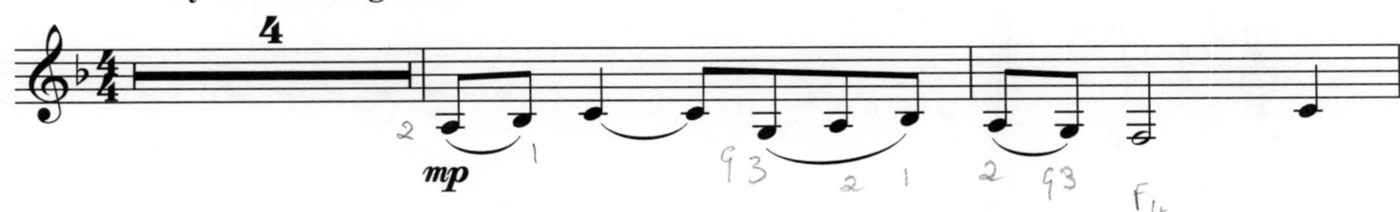
4
mp

7
f

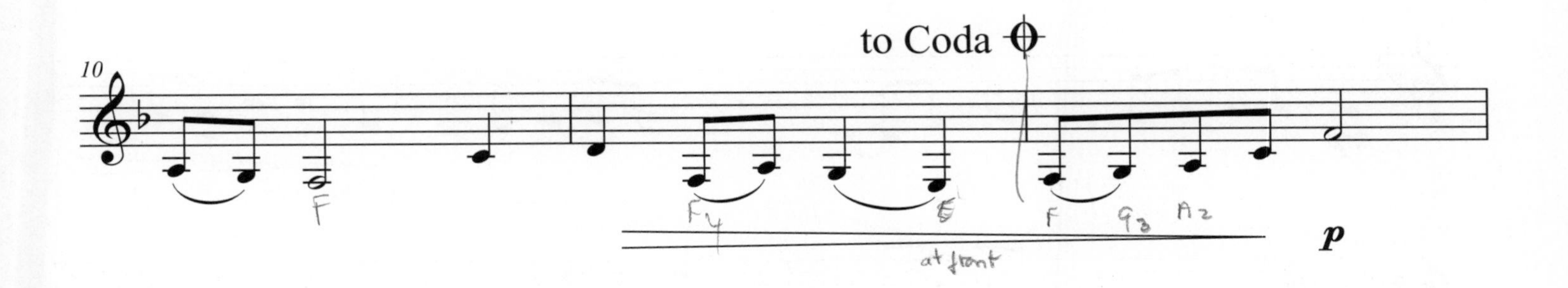
to Coda
10
p

13
mp

16
mf

D.C. al
poi al Coda
CODA
poco rit.
19
p

rehearsal 12

performance 13

The red admiral

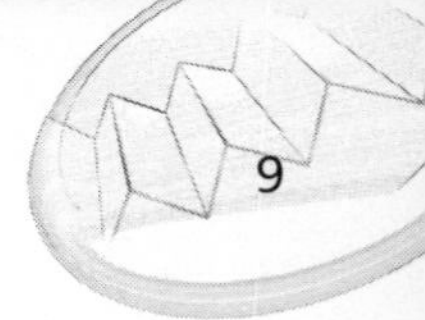

Rollerblading!

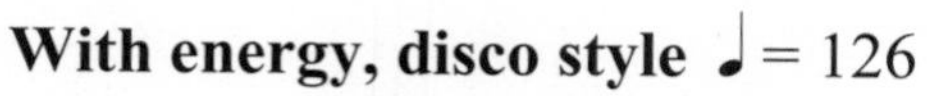

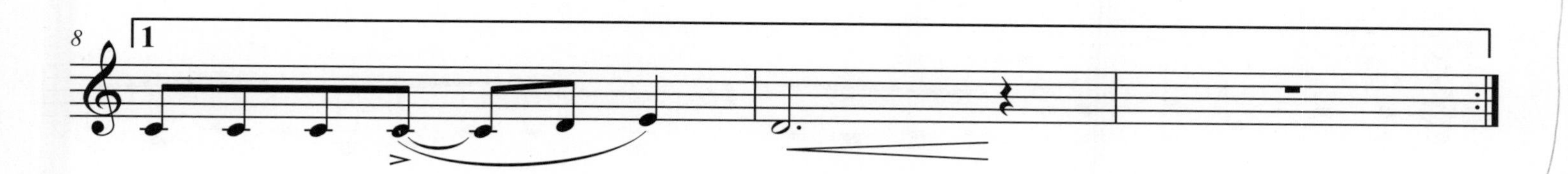

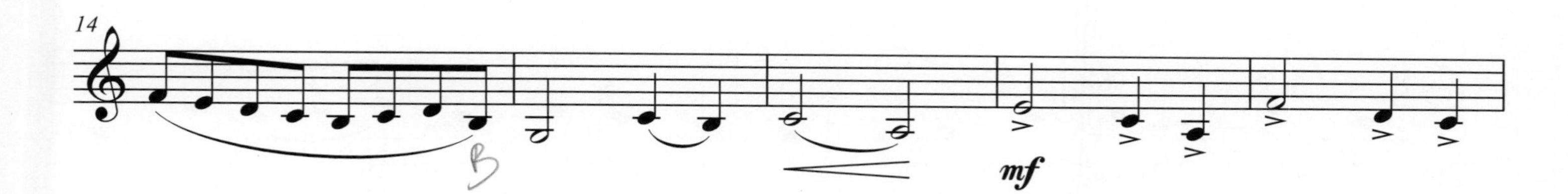

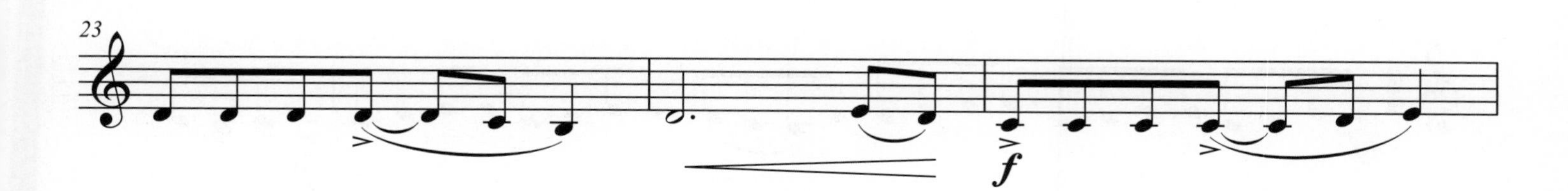

Take your partners

Make believe

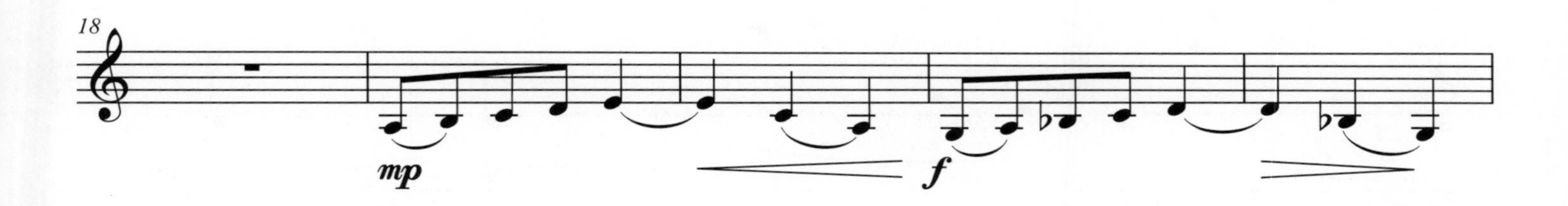

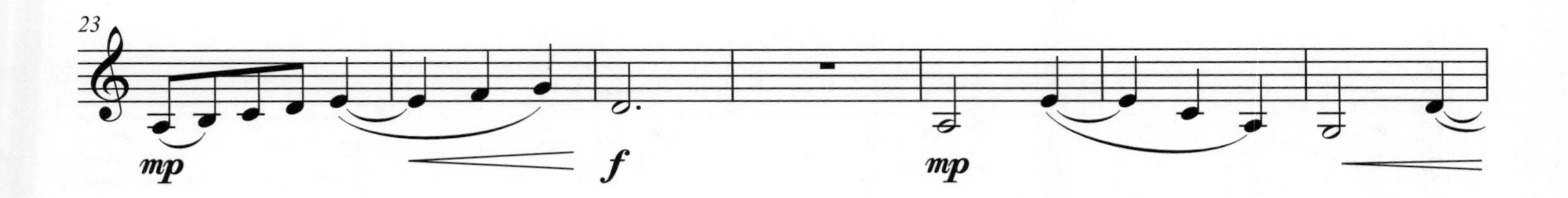

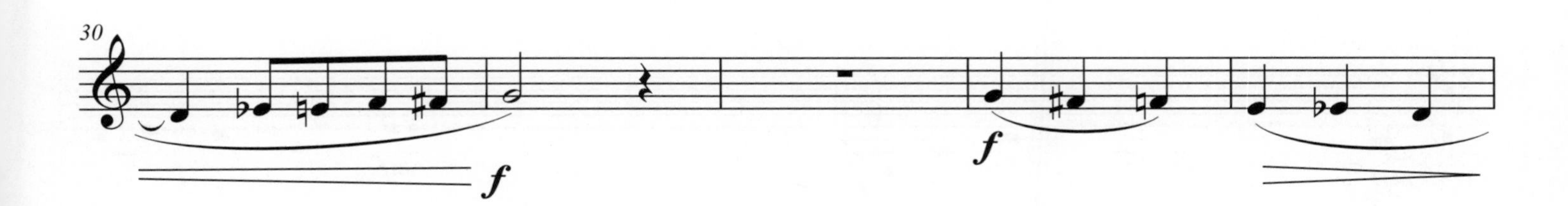

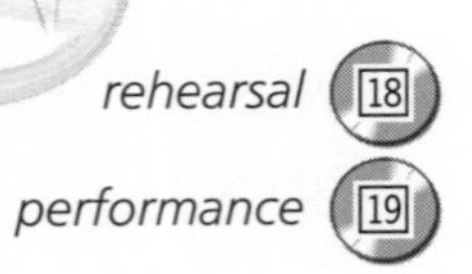
rehearsal 18
performance 19

Wild honey

Sweetly ♩ = 92
4
mp

8
f
mp

12
f

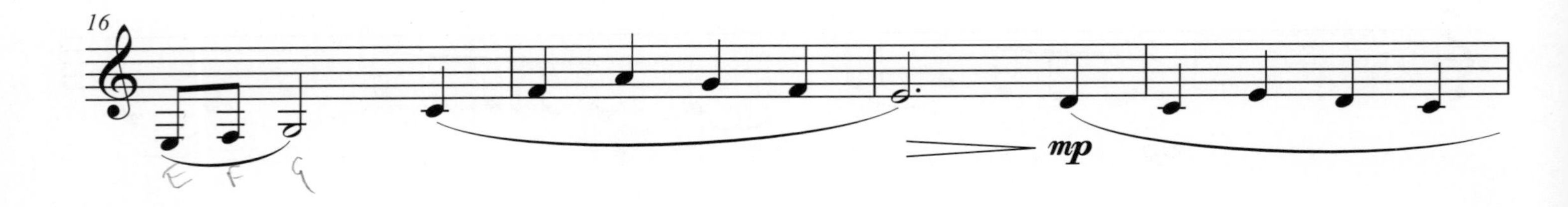
16
mp

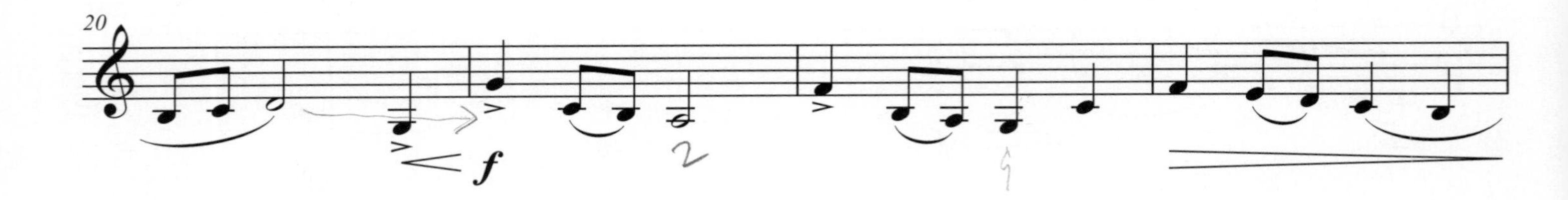
20
f

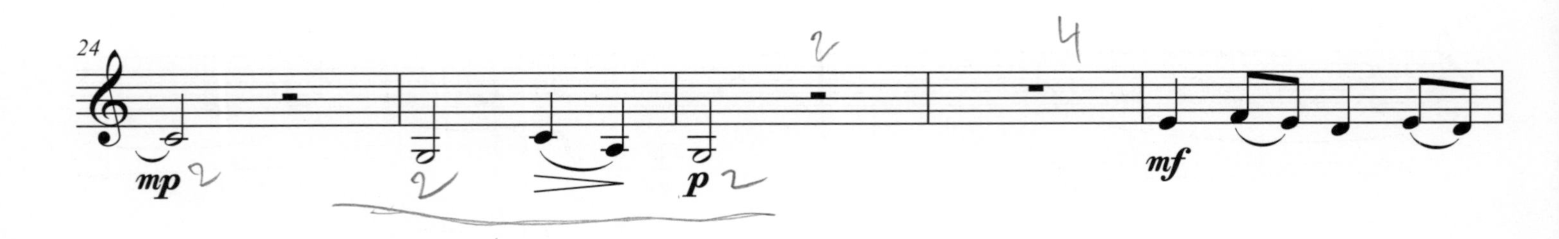
24
mp
p
mf

29
mp
p

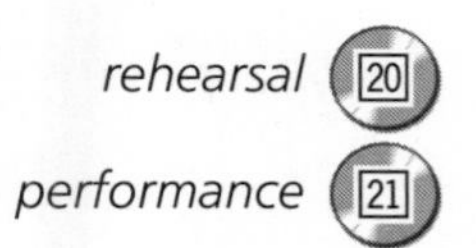

King of the swing

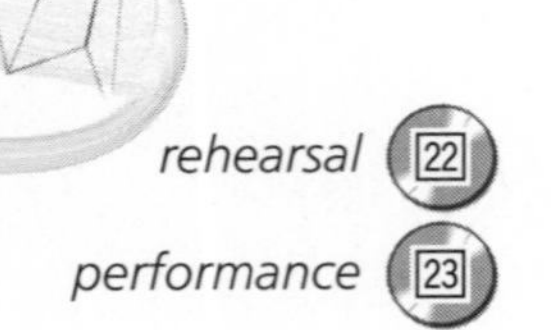

O soldier, soldier

arr. L.C.

Brighton belle

rehearsal 26
performance 27

Jig along

Lively ♩. = 108

mf f mp p mf mf f mp f p *cresc.* f